EASIEST KEYBOARD COLLECTION

21st Century Hits

WISE PUBLICATIONS
part of The Music Sales Group
London/New York/Paris/Sydney/Copenhagen/Berlin/Madrid/Tokyo

AMERICAN BOY

Words & Music by Estelle Swaray, Kanye West, Keith Harris, Will Adams, Josh Lopez,
Caleb Speir, John Stephens, & Kweli Washington

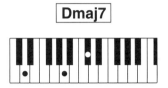
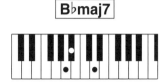
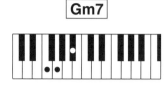
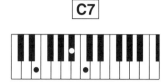

Voice: **Electric Piano**

Rhythm: **Bossa Nova**

Tempo: ♩ = 118

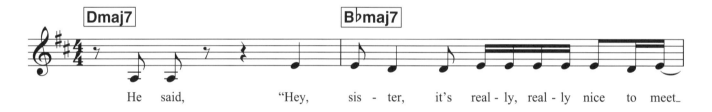

BEAT AGAIN

Words & Music by Wayne Hector & Steve Mac

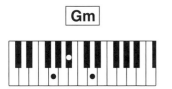
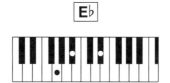
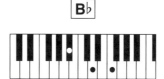
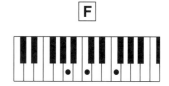

Voice: **Ocarina**

Rhythm: **Heavy Metal**

Tempo: ♩ = 120

Damn, the doc-tor's just fin-ished tell-ing me there's no time; los-ing you

could be the end of me, and that I should do the things that I wan-na do. How could

I with-out you, with-out you, oh?_____ Oh,___ 'cause

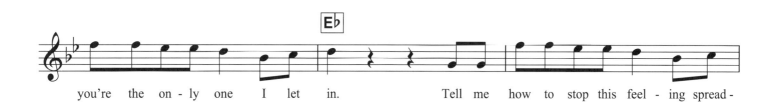

you're the on-ly one I let in. Tell me how to stop this feel-ing spread-

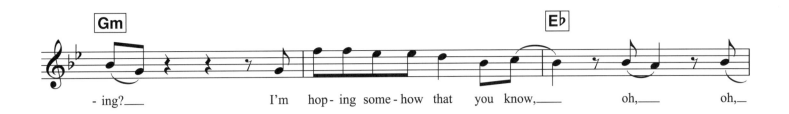

- ing?___ I'm hop-ing some-how that you know,___ oh,___ oh,___

___ oh.___ Let's just get back to-geth-er, we should-'ve nev-er broke up.

They're tell-ing me that my heart won't beat a-gain.___ We should-'ve stayed to-geth-er,

'cause when you left me it stopped. They're tell-ing me that my

heart won't beat a-gain,___ won't beat a-gain.___ It's kill-ing me.___

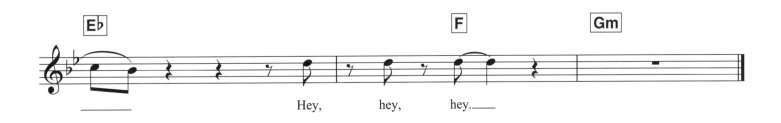

___ Hey, hey, hey.___

BEDSHAPED

Words & Music by Tim Rice-Oxley, Tom Chaplin, Richard Hughes & James Sanger

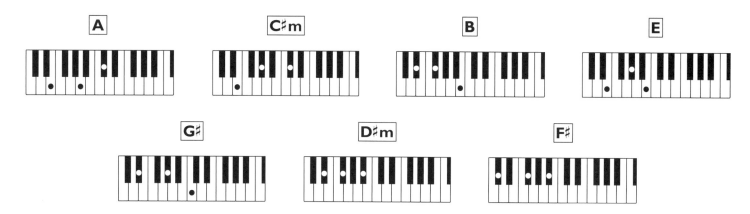

Voice: **Flute**

Rhythm: **Folk Rock**

Tempo: ♩ = 80

Man-y's the time___ I ran___ with you down___ the rain-

- y roads___ of our___ old town.___

Man - y the lives___ we lived___ in each day_____ and bu-

- ried al - to-geth - er. Don't laugh at me.___

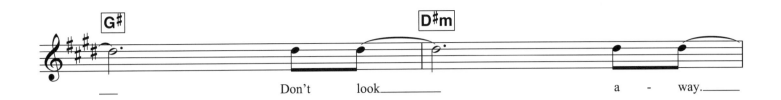

G#   D#m

Don't look_____   a - way._____

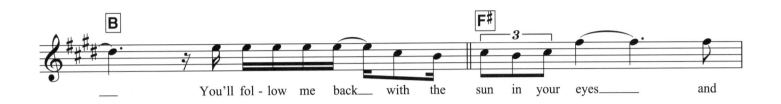

B   F#
                                        3

You'll fol - low me back__ with the sun in your eyes_____   and

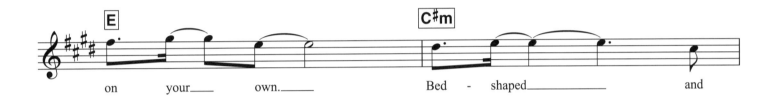

E   C#m

on   your___ own._____   Bed - shaped_____   and

B   F#
                                        3

legs of___ stone.___   You'll knock on my door_____   and

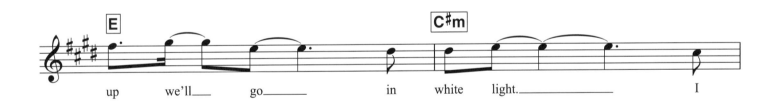

E   C#m

up we'll___ go_____   in white light._____   I

B   A

don't think___ so._____   But what___ do I___ know?_____

F#m   E

What do I___ know?_____   I know._____

DOMINOS

Words & Music by Robbie Furze & Milo Cordell

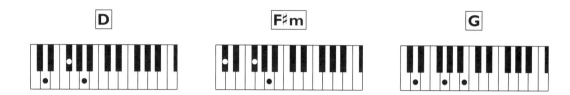

Voice: **Electric Piano**

Rhythm: **Slow Rock**

Tempo: ♩ = 100

These girls fall___ like do - mi - nos,___ do - mi - nos.___

These girls fall___ like do - mi - nos,___ do - mi - nos.___

These girls fall___ like do - mi - nos,___ do - mi - nos.___

As soon as___ I

love her it's been too___ long,___ talks of

fu - ture with you caves me___ in.___ Swal - low my

su - gar kiss and eat it a - lone.___ Hearts col - lide and

F#m **G**

smash an - y dreams of love.___ These girls fall___ like

do - mi - nos,___ do - mi - nos.___ These girls fall___ like

D **F#m** **G**

do - mi - nos,___ do - mi - nos.___ These girls fall___ like

D

do - mi - nos,___ do - mi - nos,___ do - mi - nos.___

ECLIPSE (ALL YOURS)

Words by Emily Haines & James Shaw
Music by Emily Haines, James Shaw & Howard Shore

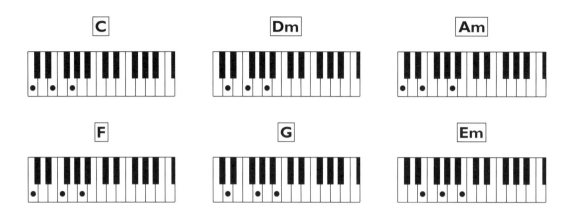

Voice: **Flute**

Rhythm: **Rock 2**

Tempo: ♩ = **130**

All the lives____ al-ways temp - ted to trade.____

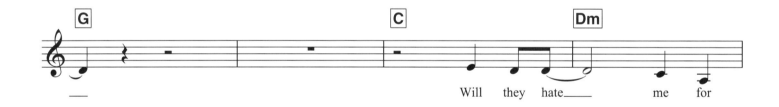

____ Will they hate____ me for

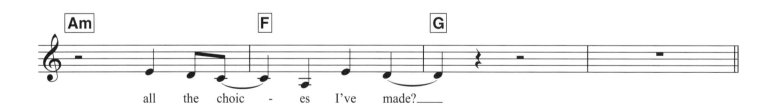

all the choic - es I've made?____

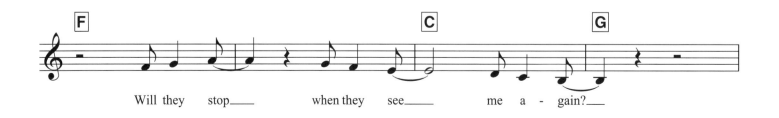

Will they stop____ when they see____ me a - gain?____

I can't stop_____ now I know_____

__ who I am._____ Now

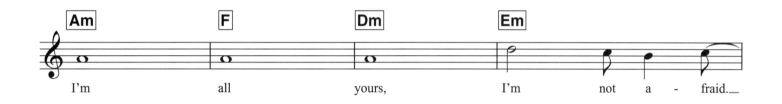

I'm all yours, I'm not a - fraid.__

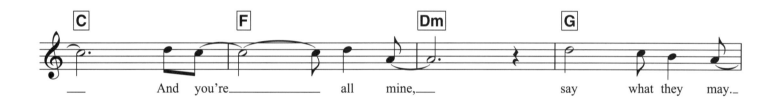

__ And you're_____ all mine,__ say what they may._

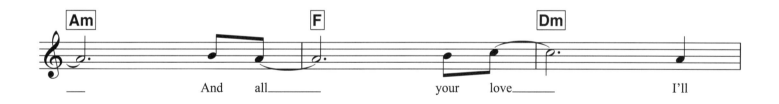

__ And all_____ your love_____ I'll

take to a grave.__ And all_____ my life___

starts_____ now.

FORGET YOU

Words & Music by Thomas Callaway, Philip Lawrence, Peter Hernandez, Ari Levine & Christopher Brown

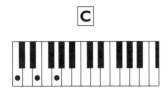
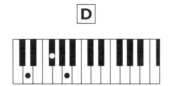
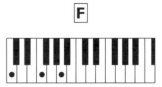

Voice: **Accordion**

Rhythm: **Rock**

Tempo: ♩ = 102

I see you driv- ing 'round town with the girl I love___ and I'm like,___

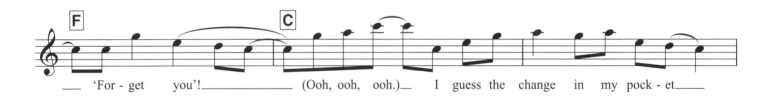

___ 'For - get you'!_____ (Ooh, ooh, ooh.)___ I guess the change in my pock - et___

was - n't e - nough.__ I'm like,___ 'For - get you! And for - get her too'. I said,

if I was rich - er,___ I'd still be with__ ya.__ Ha, now ain't that some...

(Ain't that some...) And al - though there's pain in my chest I still___

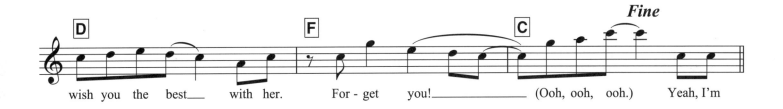

wish you the best___ with her. For - get you!_____ (Ooh, ooh, ooh.) Yeah, I'm

sor - ry, I can't af - ford a Fer - ra - ri, but

that don't mean I can't get you there.___ I guess he's an

X - box and I'm more like A - ta - ri. Mm, but the

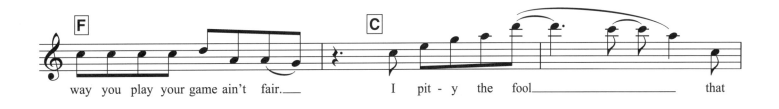

way you play your game ain't fair.___ I pit - y the fool___ that

falls in love with you,___ oh. (Oh, she's a gold dig- ger.) Well... (Just thought you should know...)

Ooh.___ I've got some news for you:___

13

FOUNDATIONS

Words & Music by Kate Nash & Paul Epworth

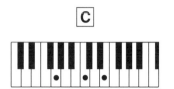
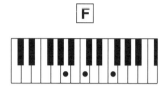
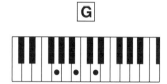
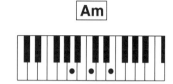

Voice: **Trumpet**

Rhythm: **Mersey Beat**

Tempo: ♩ = 168

Thurs - day___ night, ev - 'ry -thing's fine, ex - cept you've___ got that

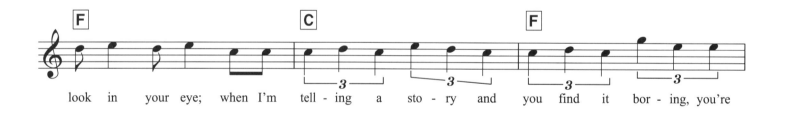

look in your eye; when I'm tell - ing a sto - ry and you find it bor - ing, you're

think - ing of some - thing to___ say. You go a - long with it___ then drop___

___ it and hu - mil - i - ate___ me in front___ of our___

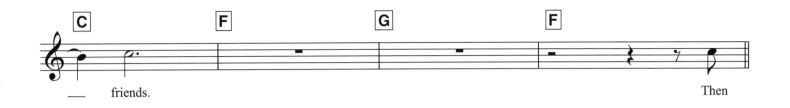

_ friends.   Then

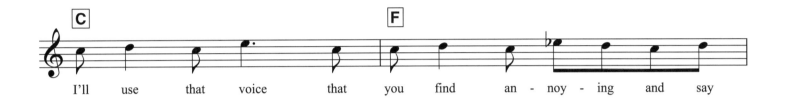

I'll   use   that   voice   that   you   find   an - noy - ing   and   say

some - thing   like: _(Spoken:)_ _"Yeah, intelligent input, darling._   _Why don't you just have another beer, then?"_

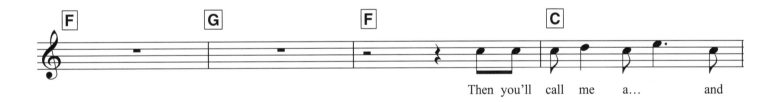

Then   you'll   call   me   a...   and

ev - 'ry - one   we're___   with   will   be   em - bar - rassed,   and   I   won't___   give   a...

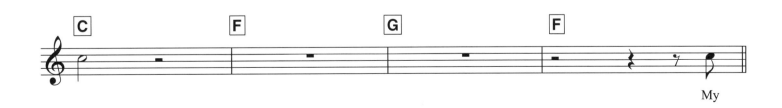

My

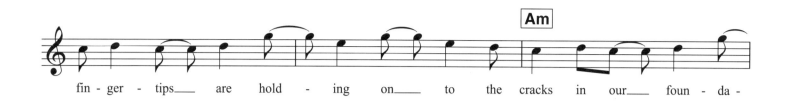

fin - ger - tips___ are hold - ing on___ to the cracks in our___ foun - da -

- tions, and I know that I___ should let___ go, but I___

___ can't. And ev - 'ry time___ we fight___

___ I know___ it's not right, ev - 'ry time that you're

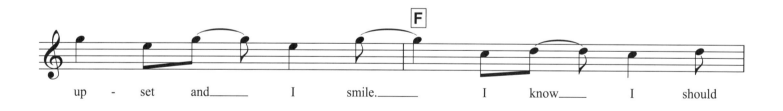

up - set and___ I smile.___ I know___ I should

for - get,___ but I___ can't.

I BELIEVE IN YOU

Words & Music by Kylie Minogue, Jason Sellards & Scott Hoffman

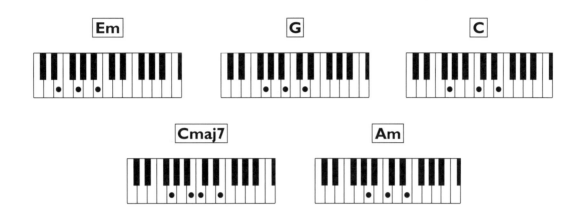

Voice: **Bright Pad**

Rhythm: **Pop Rock 2**

Tempo: ♩ = 120

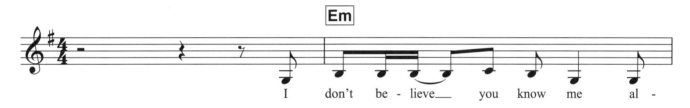

I don't be-lieve___ you know me al-

-though you know___ my name, I don't be-lieve___ the faults I have are on-ly mine to blame. I

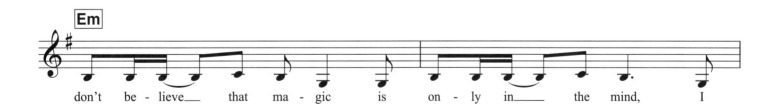

don't be-lieve___ that ma-gic is on-ly in___ the mind, I

don't be-lieve___ I'd love some-bod-y just to pass the time. But I___

be - lieve in you.

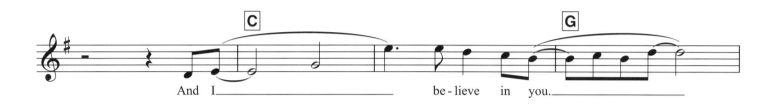

And I be - lieve in you.

But I be - lieve in

you. And I

be - lieve in you.

And if you ev - er had to go a - way, noth - ing in my world could ev - er

be the same.___ Noth-ing lasts for ev-er but to-geth-er till then,___ I'll

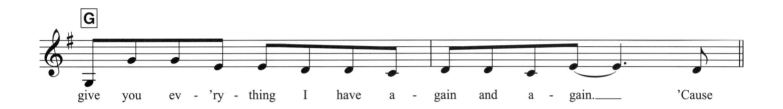

give you ev-'ry-thing I have a-gain and a-gain.___ 'Cause

I be-lieve___ in you,___ I be-lieve in.

I be-lieve___ in you,___ I be-lieve in. I be-lieve___ in you,___

___ I be-lieve in. I be-lieve___ in you,___ I be-lieve in.

I be-lieve,___ I be-lieve___ in you.

HEY YA!

Words & Music by André Benjamin

© Copyright 2003 Gnat Booty Music, USA.
Chrysalis Music Limited.
All Rights Reserved. International Copyright Secured.

C   F   G   Am

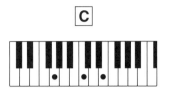 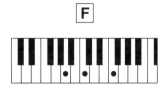 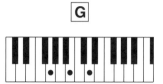 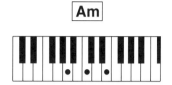

Voice: **Accordion**

Rhythm: **Rock**

Tempo: ♩ = 102

My ba-by don't mess a - round__ be-cause she loves me so__ and this I

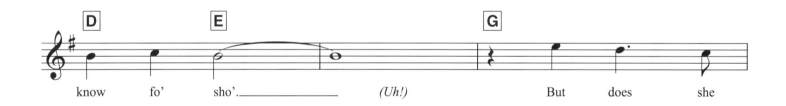

know fo' sho'._____ *(Uh!)* But does she

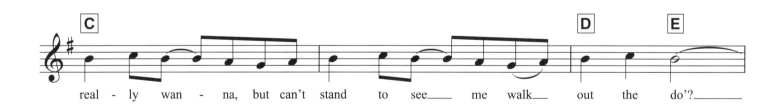

real - ly wan - na, but can't stand to see__ me walk__ out the do'?__

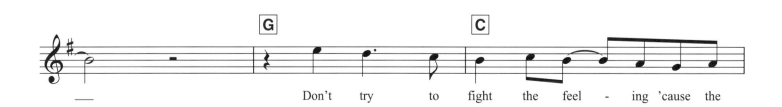

__ Don't try to fight the feel - ing 'cause the

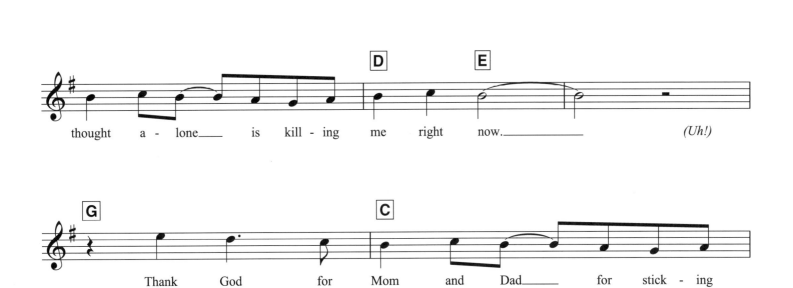

thought a - lone___ is kill - ing me right now._____ *(Uh!)*

Thank God for Mom and Dad___ for stick - ing

two to - geth - er 'cause we don't know how._____ *(C'mon!)*

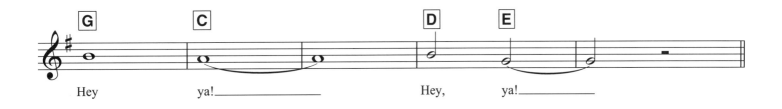

Hey ya!_____ Hey, ya!_____

Hey ya!_____ Hey, ya!_____

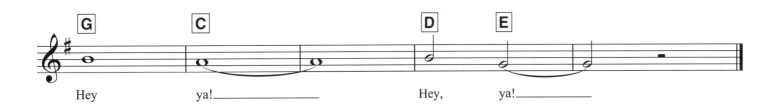

Hey ya!_____ Hey, ya!_____

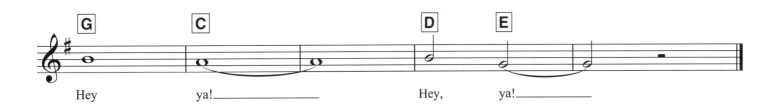

Hey ya!_____ Hey, ya!_____

JUST DANCE

Words & Music by Aliaune Thiam, Stefani Germanotta & Nadir Khayat

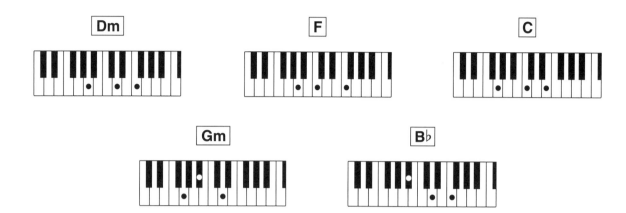

Voice: **Power Lead**

Rhythm: **Disco**

Tempo: ♩ = 116

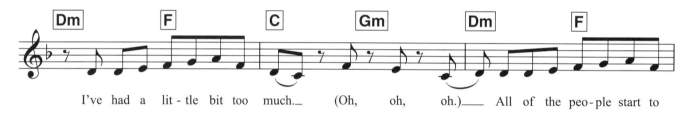

I've had a lit-tle bit too much.__ (Oh, oh, oh.)__ All of the peo-ple start to

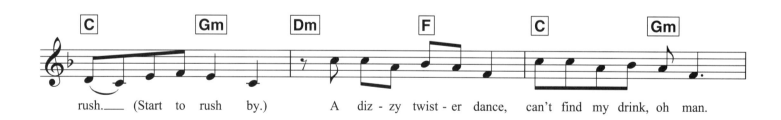

rush.__ (Start to rush by.) A diz-zy twist-er dance, can't find my drink, oh man.

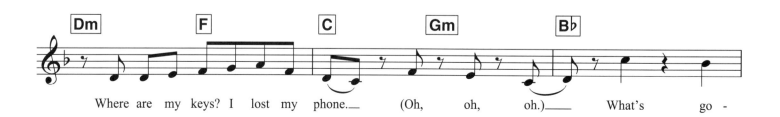

Where are my keys? I lost my phone.__ (Oh, oh, oh.)__ What's go -

- ing on on the floor?_____ I love this rec - ord, ba - by,

but I can't see straight an - y - more._____ Keep it cool. What's the name of this club?_

___ I can't re - mem - ber, but it's al - right, a - al - right. Just

dance,___ gon - na be o - kay. Da doo doo. Just dance,___ spin that rec - ord, babe.

Da da doo doo, mm. Just dance,___ gon - na be o - kay. D - d - d - dance.___

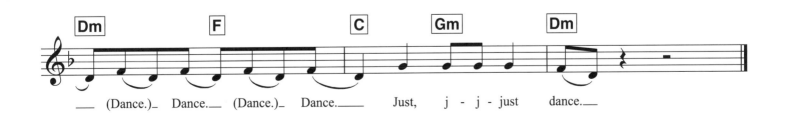

___ (Dance.)_ Dance.__ (Dance.)_ Dance.____ Just, j - j - just dance.___

MAPS

Words & Music by Karen O, Nicholas Zinner & Brian Chase

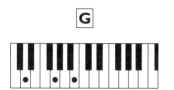 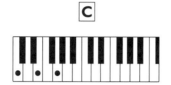 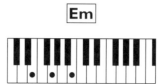 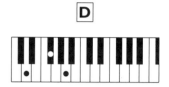

Voice: **Electric Guitar**

Rhythm: **Folk Rock**

Tempo: ♩ = 120

Pack___ up, I'm___ straight, I'm___

not. Oh,____ say say say you'll,____

say say say you'll,____ say say say you'll,____

say say say you'll,____ say say say...

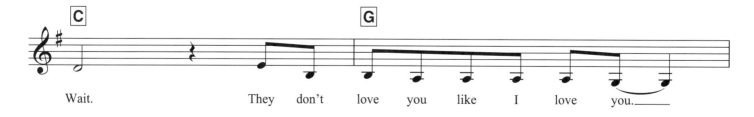

Wait. They don't love you like I love you.____

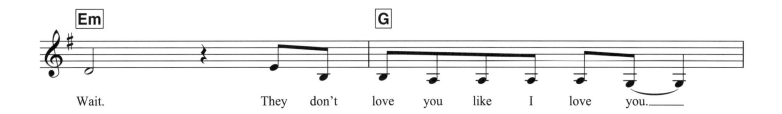

Wait. They don't love you like I love you.

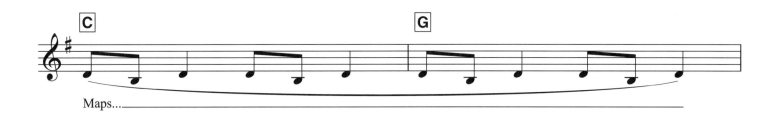

Maps....

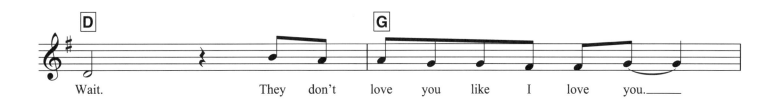

Wait. They don't love you like I love you.

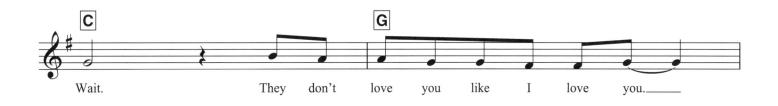

Wait. They don't love you like I love you.

Maps....

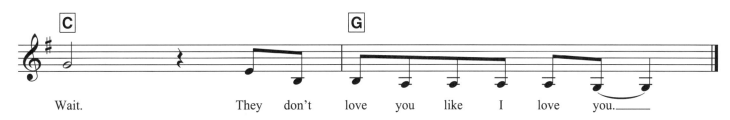

Wait. They don't love you like I love you.

MYKONOS

Words & Music by Robin Pecknold
© Copyright 2008 Chrysalis Music Limited.
All Rights Reserved. International Copyright Secured.

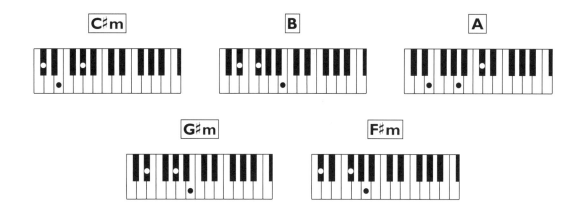

Voice: **Acoustic Guitar**

Rhythm: **Slow Rock**

Tempo: ♩ = 120

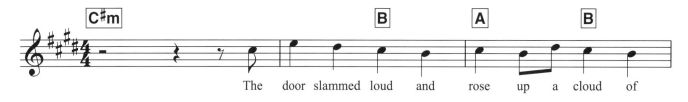

The door slammed loud and rose up a cloud of

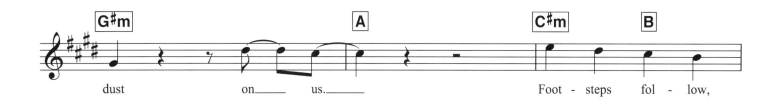

dust on us. Foot - steps fol - low,

down through the hol - low sound, torn up. And you

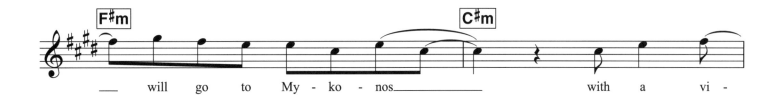

_____ will go to My - ko - nos_____ with a vi -

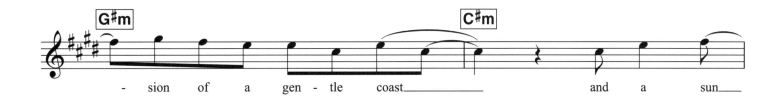

_____ sion of a gen - tle coast_____ and a sun___

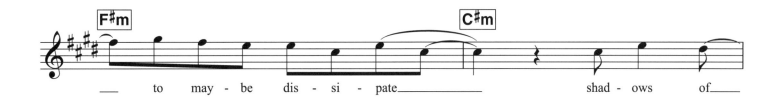

_____ to may - be dis - si - pate_____ shad - ows of___

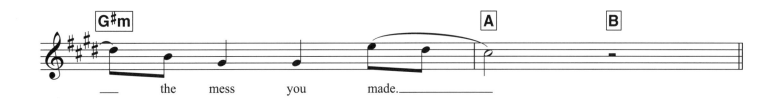

___ the mess you made._____

Oh,_____ oh,___

_____ oh._____

THE ONE I LOVE

Words & Music by David Gray & Craig McClune

Voice: **Alto Saxophone**

Rhythm: **Slow Rock**

Tempo: ♩ = 108

RUDE BOY

Words & Music by Mikkel S. Eriksen, Tor Erik Hermansen, Makeba Riddick, Esther Dean, Rob Swire & Robyn Fenty

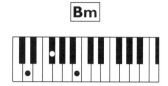
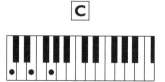
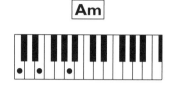

Voice: **Alto Saxophone**

Rhythm: **Drum & Bass**

Tempo: ♩ = 96

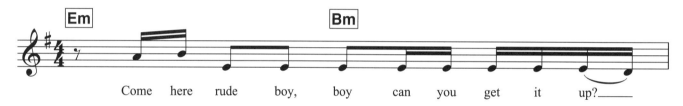

Come here rude boy, boy can you get it up?____

Come here rude boy, boy is you big e-nough?_ Take it, take it, ba-by, ba-by.

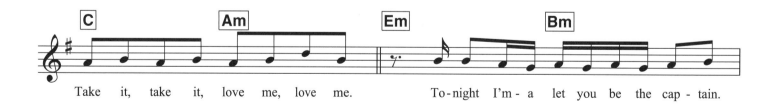

Take it, take it, love me, love me. To-night I'm-a let you be the cap-tain.

To-night I'm-ma let you do your thing, yeah. To-night I'm-a let you be a rid-er.

Gid - dy up,   gid - dy up,   gid - dy up, ____ babe.

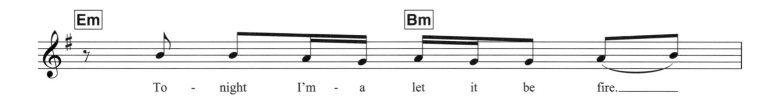

To - night I'm - a let it be fire. _____

To - night I'm - a let you take me high - er.   To - night, ba - by, we can get it on, yeah.

We can get it on,   yeah. ____ Do you like it boy? I

wa - wa - want what you wa - wa - want.   Give it to me, ba - by, like boom, boom, boom. What I

wa - wa - want is what you wa - wa - want. Na, nah. _____

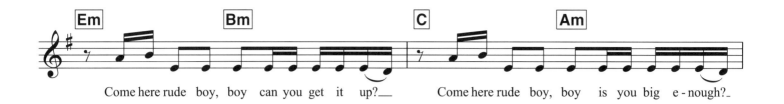

Come here rude boy, boy can you get it up?__ Come here rude boy, boy is you big e-nough?_

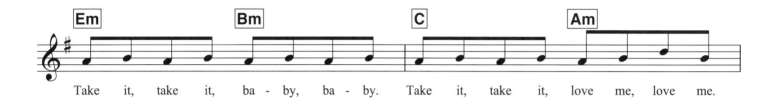

Take it, take it, ba-by, ba-by. Take it, take it, love me, love me.

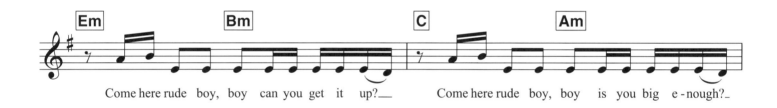

Come here rude boy, boy can you get it up?__ Come here rude boy, boy is you big e-nough?_

Take it, take it, ba-by, ba-by. Take it, take it, love me, love me. Love me, love me. love me, love me,

love me, love me, love me, love me. Take it, take it, ba-by, ba-by. Take it, take it, love me, love me.

SOMEONE LIKE YOU

Words & Music by Adele Adkins & Daniel Wilson

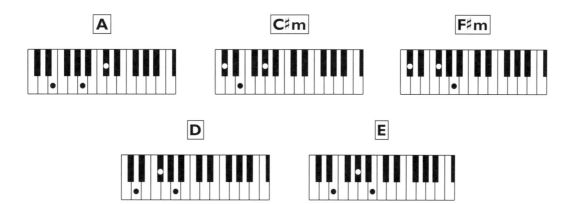

Voice: **Piano**

Rhythm: **Blues Rock**

Tempo: ♩ = 75

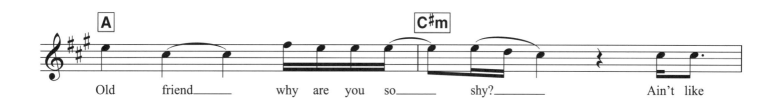

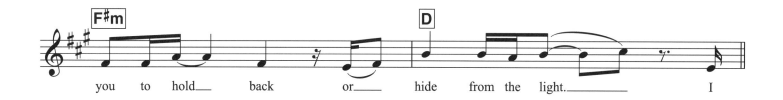

you to hold___ back or___ hide from the light._____ I

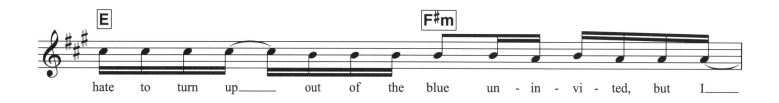

hate to turn up___ out of the blue un - in - vi - ted, but I___

___ could - n't stay a - way___ I could - n't fight it. I had

hoped you'd see my face and that you'd be re - min - ded that for

me it is - n't o - ver._____

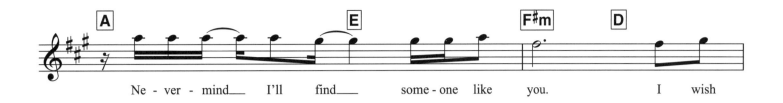

Ne - ver - mind___ I'll find___ some - one like you. I wish

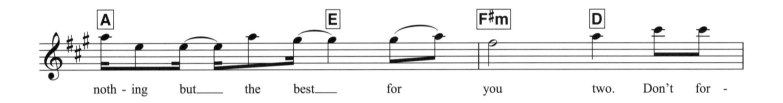

noth - ing but___ the best___ for you two. Don't for -

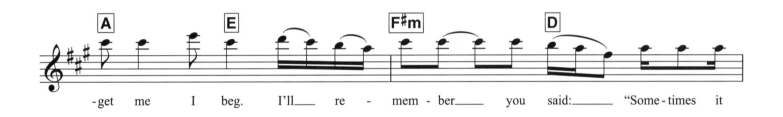

-get me I beg. I'll___ re - mem - ber___ you said:___ "Some - times it

lasts and loves but some - times it hurts in - stead." Some - times it

lasts and loves but some - times it hurts in - stead,_____

STANDING IN THE WAY OF CONTROL

Words & Music by Beth Ditto, Nathan Howdeshell & Hannah Blilie

 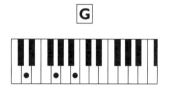 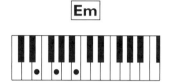 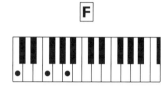

Voice: **Electric Guitar**

Rhythm: **Rock 1**

Tempo: ♩ = 120

Your back's a - gainst the wall. There's

no one home to call. You're for - get - ting who you are. You

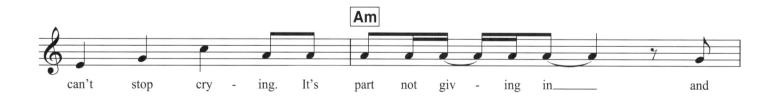

can't stop cry - ing. It's part not giv - ing in and

part trust - ing your friends. You do it all a - gain and

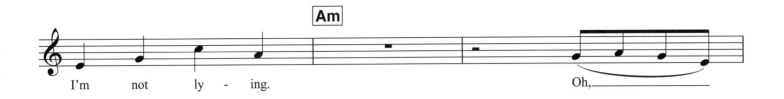

I'm not ly - ing. Oh,_____

oh,_____ ooh._____ Oh,_____

_ oh,_____ oh,_____ ooh._____

Stand - ing in the way of con - trol._____ Yeah,___ live your lives sur -

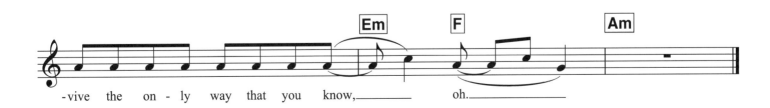

-vive the on - ly way that you know,_____ oh._____

STEADY, AS SHE GOES

Words & Music by Jack White & Brendan Benson
© Copyright 2006 Gladsad Music/Third String Tunes, USA
Chrysalis Music Limited (50%)/EMI Music Publishing Limited (50%).
All Rights Reserved. International Copyright Secured.

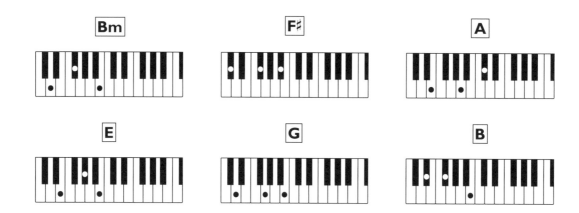

Voice: **Rock Organ**

Rhythm: **Hard Rock**

Tempo: ♩ = 130

Find your-self a girl,___ and set-tle down.___ Live a sim-ple

life___ in a qui-et town.___ Stead-y as she

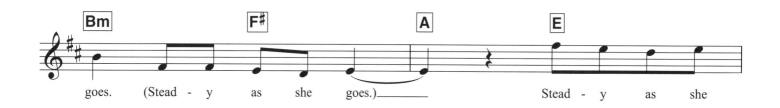

goes. (Stead-y as she goes.)___ Stead-y as she

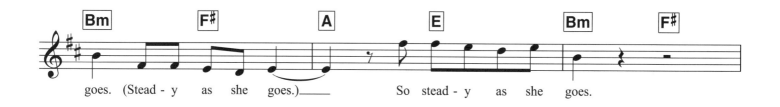

goes. (Stead-y as she goes.)___ So stead-y as she goes.

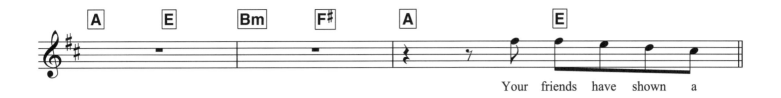

Your friends have shown a

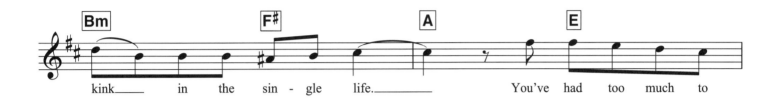

kink____ in the sin - gle life._____ You've had too much to

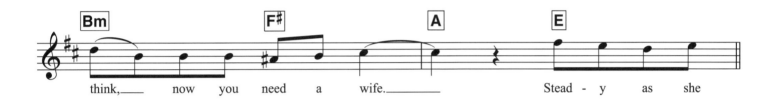

think,____ now you need a wife._____ Stead - y as she

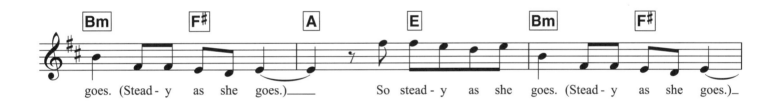

goes. (Stead - y as she goes.)____ So stead - y as she goes. (Stead - y as she goes.)__

Well, here we go a - gain,__ you've found your - self____ a friend that knows you__ well..

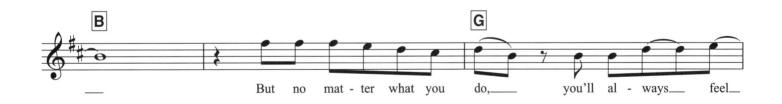

But no mat - ter what you do,____ you'll al - ways__ feel__

as though you tripped and__ fell.____ So stead - y as she goes.

STRONGER

Words & Music by Mutya Buena, Keisha Buchanan, Heidi Range, Marius De Vries, Felix Howard & Jony Rockstar

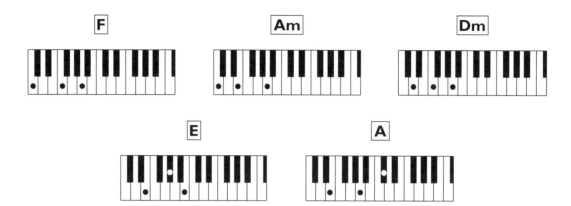

Voice: **New Age Pad**

Rhythm: **Electro Pop**

Tempo: ♩ = 85

I'll make it through the rain - y days.___ I'll be the one_

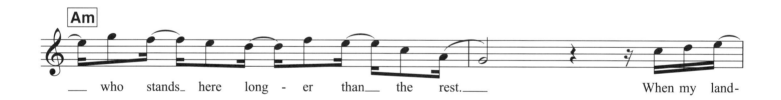

__ who stands_ here long - er than_ the rest.___ When my land-

-scape chan - ges, re - ar - ran - ges, I'll be strong - er than I've ev - er been.__

No more still - ness, more sun - light.__ Ev -'ry - thing_ is gon - na be al - right._____

I know_____ that there's gon - na be_____ a change._____ Bet - ter find_

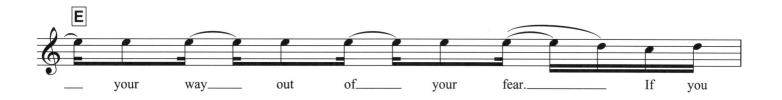

___ your way_____ out of_____ your fear._____ If you

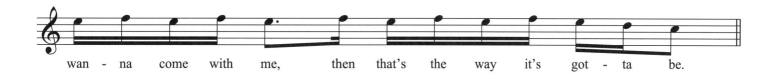

wan - na come with me, then that's the way it's got - ta be.

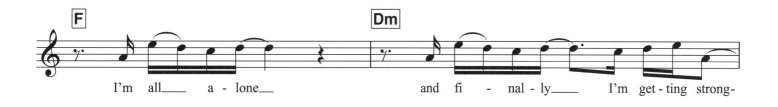

I'm all___ a - lone___ and fi - nal - ly___ I'm get - ting strong-

- er.___ You'll come to see___ just what I can be._

_____ I'm get - ting strong - er.___

TROUBLE

Words & Music by Ray LaMontagne

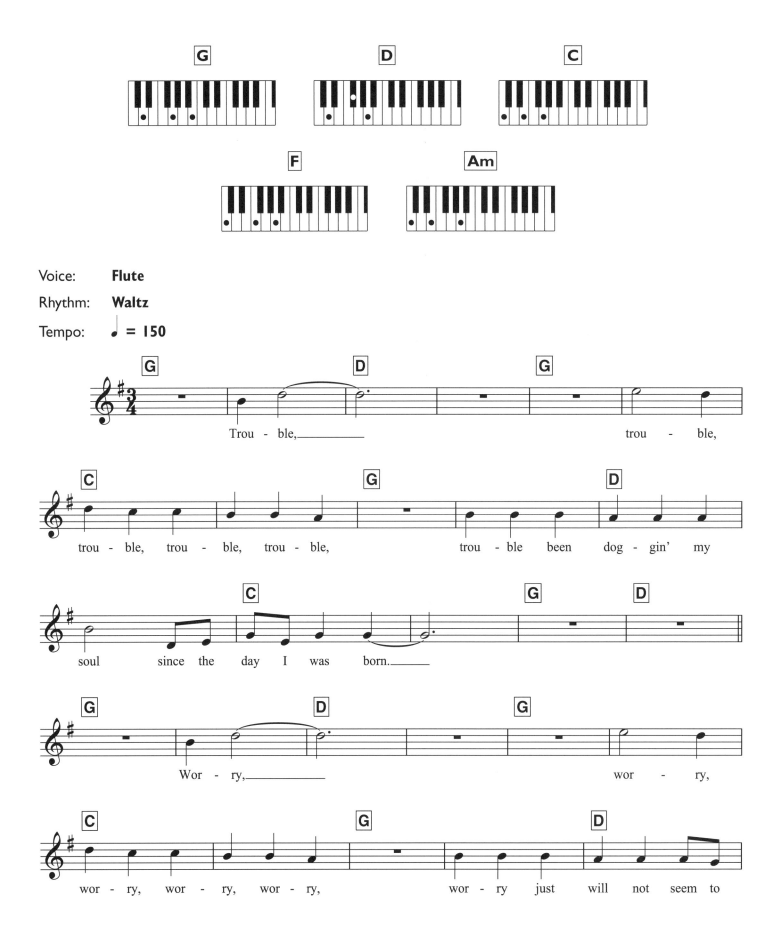

Voice: **Flute**

Rhythm: **Waltz**

Tempo: ♩ = 150

TUMBLE AND FALL

Words & Music by Grant Nicholas

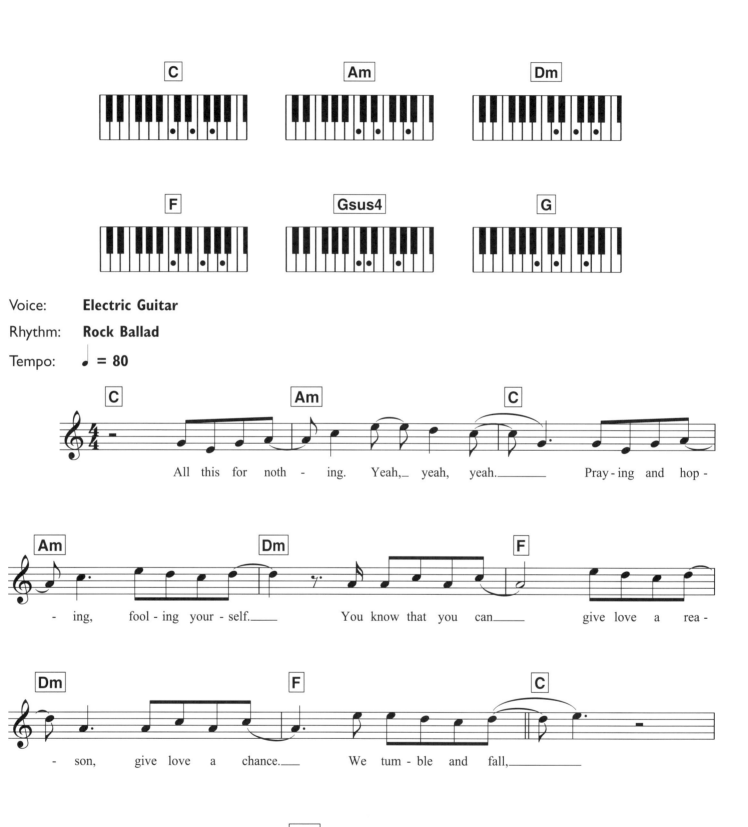

Voice: **Electric Guitar**

Rhythm: **Rock Ballad**

Tempo: ♩ = 80

All this for noth - ing. Yeah,_ yeah, yeah._____ Pray - ing and hop -

- ing, fool - ing your - self.___ You know that you can___ give love a rea -

- son, give love a chance.___ We tum - ble and fall,_____

to - geth - er we crawl.___ For - ev - er we'll be,_

WIRES

Words & Music by Joel Pott, Carey Willetts, Steve Roberts & Tim Wanstall

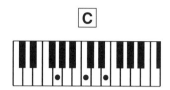

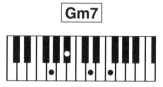

Voice: **Piano**

Rhythm: **Love Ballad**

Tempo: ♩ = 66

You got wires go - ing in, you got wires com - ing

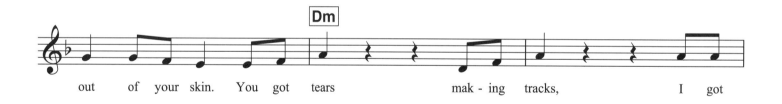

out of your skin. You got tears mak - ing tracks, I got

tears that are scared of the facts. Run - ning down cor - ri - dors, through

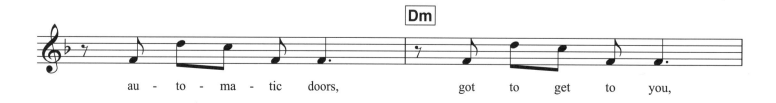

au - to - ma - tic doors, got to get to you,

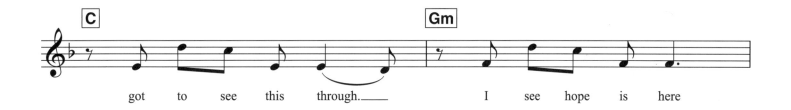

got to see this through.____ I see hope is here

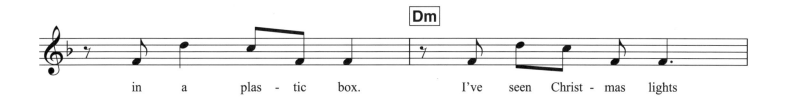

in a plas - tic box. I've seen Christ - mas lights

ref - lect in your eyes. I see it in your____

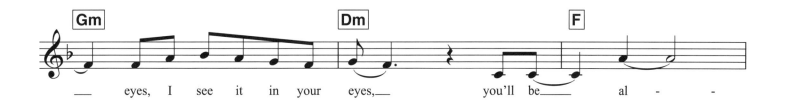

____ eyes, I see it in your eyes,____ you'll be____ al - -

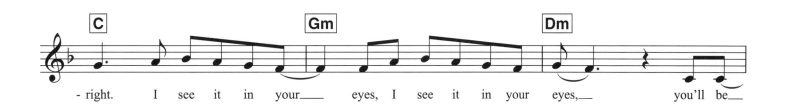

- right. I see it in your____ eyes, I see it in your eyes,____ you'll be____

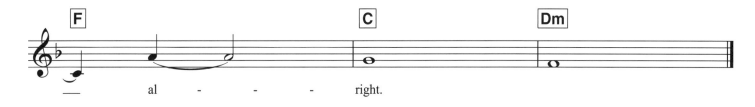

____ al - - - right.

Published by
Wise Publications

Exclusive Distributors:
Music Sales Limited
14-15 Berners Street,
London W1T 3LJ, UK.
Music Sales Pty Limited
20 Resolution Drive,
Caringbah, NSW 2229, Australia.

Order No. AM1003145
ISBN: 978-1-78038-023-0
This book © Copyright 2011 Wise Publications.

Edited by Jenni Wheeler.
Music processed by Paul Ewers Music Design.

Printed in the EU.

Your Guarantee of Quality
As publishers, we strive to produce every book to the highest
commercial standards.
Particular care has been given to specifying acid-free, neutral-sized
paper made from pulps which have not been elemental chlorine
bleached. This pulp is from farmed sustainable forests and was
produced with special regard for the environment.
Throughout, the printing and binding have been planned to ensure
a sturdy, attractive publication which should give years of enjoyment.
If your copy fails to meet our high standards, please inform us and
we will gladly replace it.

www.musicsales.com